# When Dad Died

## Sheila Hollins and Lester Sireling
## illustrated by Beth Webb

Beyond Words

London

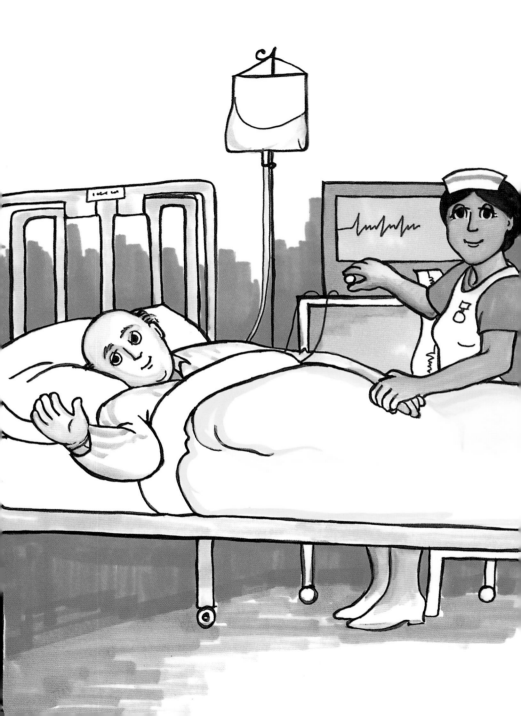

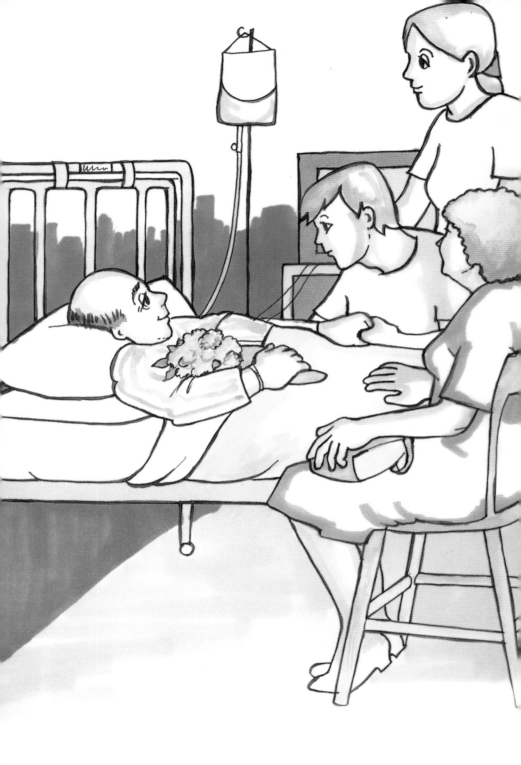

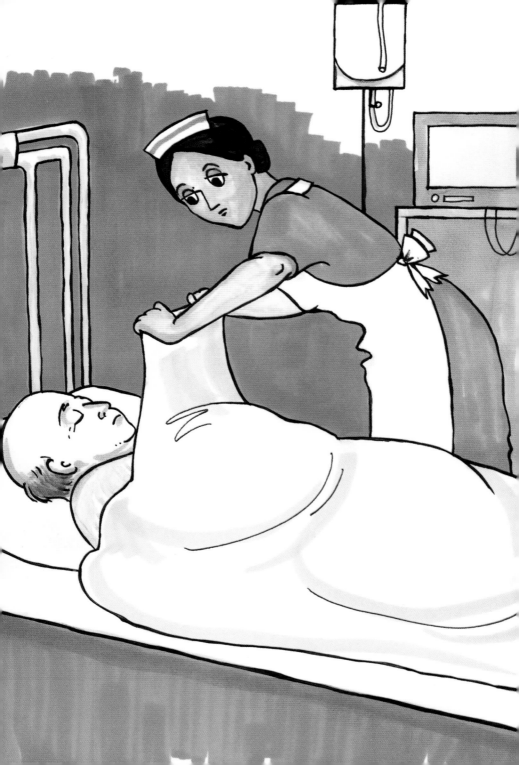

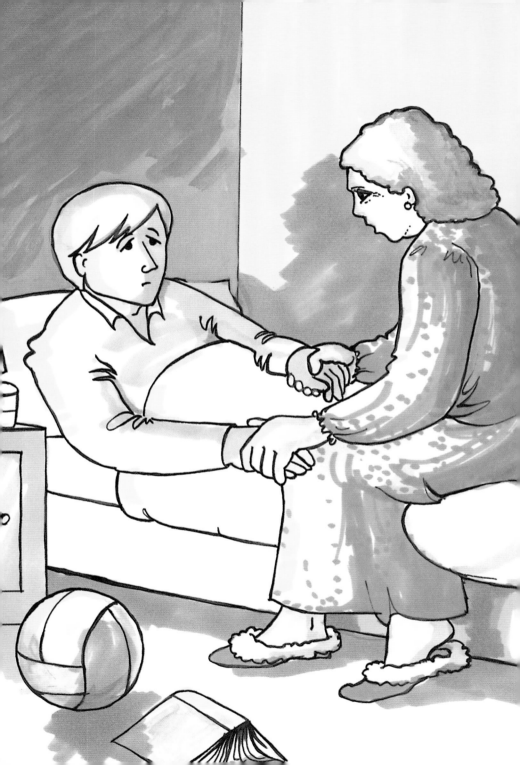

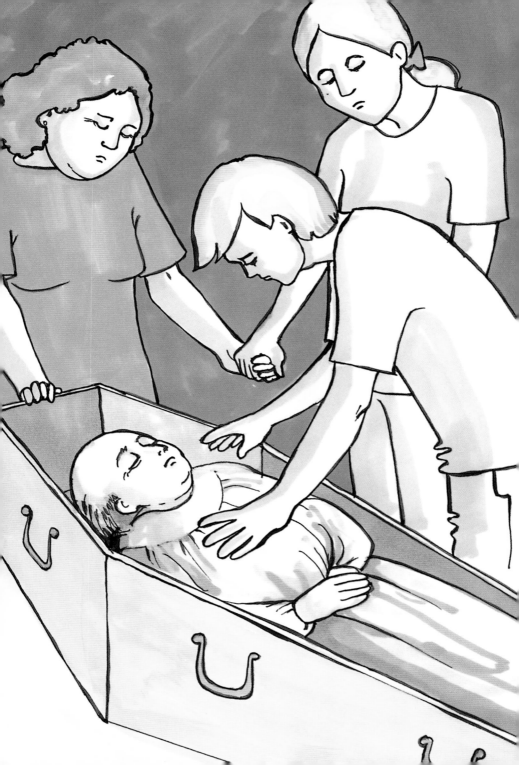

First edition 1989, St George's Mental Health Library in association with Silent Books.

Second edition 1994, St George's Mental Health Library.

Third revised edition 2004, Gaskell and St George's Hospital Medical School.

This edition published 2014 by Books Beyond Words.

ISBN 978-1-78458-002-5

**British Library Cataloguing-in-Publication Data**
A catalogue record for this book is available from the British Library.

Printed by DX Imaging, Watford.

Books Beyond Words is a Community Interest Company registered in England and Wales (7557861).

St George's Hospital Charity is a registered charity (no. 241527).

# Contents

**The following words are provided for people who want a ready-made story rather than tell their own.**

1. This is a picture of Stephen with his family. The story tells us what happened when his Dad died.

2. One day Dad had a pain.

3. Mum phoned for an ambulance.

4. The ambulance came quickly and took Dad to hospital.

5. Stephen and Julie went to hospital to see Dad.

6. They bought some flowers to cheer him up.

7. Dad was in bed because he was ill. A nurse was looking after him.

8. Dad was happy to see them. They didn't know what to say. Soon Dad got tired. That was because he was ill.

9. That evening Mum said, "Let's turn off the television and talk about Dad." Stephen didn't feel like talking. He just wanted Dad to get better.

10. Dad was very ill. He slept most of the time. Stephen sat next to his bed. He wanted to be with his Dad. Sometimes his Dad woke up and looked at him.

11. Stephen hugged his Dad. He wanted to say goodbye.

12. Mum said, "I'm worried about Dad. I don't think he'll get better."

13. Later Dad died. He was not asleep. He had stopped breathing. He couldn't walk or talk or see any more.

14. The nurse phoned Mum and told her that Dad had died. Mum was very upset.

15. Mum woke Stephen up. She had something very sad to tell him. "Dad won't come home again. He has died."

16. Stephen thought it was a mistake. He wanted to go to the hospital to see Dad. Mum wouldn't let him go. They had an argument.

17. Stephen and Julie didn't feel hungry. They both felt upset.

18. Stephen felt cross and muddled.

19. Stephen thought it must be his fault Dad had gone away. He still didn't believe his Dad was dead.

20. Mum knew why Stephen was upset. She told him again that Dad was dead. Stephen still didn't understand.

21. Next day they went to see Dad. His body was in a coffin. Then Stephen understood that he was dead.

22. Dad's coffin was driven to the cemetery. Stephen, Julie and their Mum came in a different car. Dad's friends came to say goodbye.

23. Everyone said goodbye to Dad. Stephen wondered why Dad had died. Was Dad with God?

24. The curtains closed. Then Dad's body was cremated. It was burnt until only ashes were left.

25. Sometimes Stephen felt lonely. He didn't want to be with his friends. They didn't know what to say. They were glad it wasn't their Dad who had died.

26. Stephen and Julie planted a rose bush with Dad's name on it.

27. Mum gave Stephen and Julie a photograph of Dad to keep. Stephen felt sad all over again. Mum told Stephen that Dad had wanted him to have his watch. That made him feel happy.

28. They were still a family. They had good times together, and they often talked about Dad.

# How we feel when someone dies

Most of us don't believe it when we're told that someone has died. We think, "It can't be true, it's a mistake." We feel shocked, and sometimes angry. A bit later we feel muddled. Our bodies can also get muddled up after the death of someone we know. We can have headaches, maybe we need to go to the toilet more often, we want to eat a lot or we don't want to eat anything at all and we get a peculiar feeling in the tummy, like emptiness or tightness.

Some people want to keep busy and can't sleep; other people can't do anything at all and want to stay in bed all the time. Some people forget how to do things, even things they know well, like how to get dressed or how to go to the toilet. If we get a pain anywhere we might be scared that we are dying. We have some of these feelings some of the time, and sometimes we feel OK.

Some feelings are upsetting. Anything we see, anything we think about – even a special smell or taste – can remind us of the person who died. Bad memories as well as nice memories pop up; we can feel very scared or angry. After someone dies we can feel angry with anybody, even with the person who died or other people who love us. And that can make us feel even worse.

We can have dreams about the person who died. Maybe we think we can hear them walking around, or talking to us, or we think we can see them in the street. Some people worry a lot too. They may worry that somebody else will die or that it's their fault that the person died.

These strong feelings are called 'grief'. It is OK to feel grief, and it does not mean we are going mad. You know the way your skin fixes itself after you have had a cut? First it bleeds and hurts a lot. Later a lump called a scab covers over the cut. Afterwards there is still a mark if the cut was deep. Grief is a bit like that. It is the way that our mind fixes itself after we have been hurt. First it feels very messy and hurts a lot. Then it's more at the back of our mind. Afterwards there is a sad place inside which remembers how much it hurt.

## How long does it take to get back to normal?

The feelings of being sad, angry and muddled keep getting better and worse for a few weeks before they get less strong. Then there is usually just a feeling of being sad.

But for some people it can take many months to realise that the person who died will not come back. So sometimes these strong upset feelings don't start until many months after the death. This makes it difficult for us and other people to know why we are upset.

For some people life gets back to normal very quickly after somebody else dies. This is OK. Perhaps they knew that the person was going to die, and had lots of sad feelings before the death instead of after it.

For other people the strong feelings come and go for ages – months or even years. Friends and family can get fed up with this. They don't know what to say to us, they feel shy, they don't know what's going on in our mind. But we probably need to talk about the person who died, again and again. Our friends and family need lots of patience! This is what happened to Stephen in the story.

We never completely forget somebody who was close to us. As time goes by we can remember nice things about the person without being very sad as well. But we still feel a bit sad on birthdays and at the time of year when the person died. We remember them when somebody else dies or when someone gets married or has a baby.

Look at the last picture in the story. The family is smaller, but Mum, Julie and Stephen are still together. They are able to talk about Dad. The sun is shining. Everything is OK, even though it is different without Dad.

# What happens after someone dies

If the person who died was living with you, your life will change in lots of ways. You might even have to move home. You will need time to think and talk about what would be best for you. There shouldn't be any big changes until you have decided.

What about the stuff that belonged to the person who died? Don't throw it all away! Keep things which give you good memories, even if they make you feel sad as well. At the end of the story, Mum, Stephen and Julie go through Dad's things. It makes them feel closer to each other. In the last picture Stephen is wearing Dad's watch. When he looks at it he remembers Dad. He feels happy and sad.

What happens to the person who died? We know what happens to their body. It gets buried or burnt. Do you go to a church, a mosque or a synagogue, for example? People who go to these places believe that there is part of every person which is not the body. This part – the soul or spirit of the person – does not die when the body dies. To find out more about this, ask your family or someone in the place where you go to pray.

# Is it the same when a child is bereaved?

Sometimes children aren't allowed to see very ill people, or to go to a funeral (where the dead body is buried in the ground or burnt in a special oven). Then they have to guess or make up a reason for what is going on. The trouble is, when someone is very ill or someone dies, everybody else is really upset. If you don't know what happened, because they haven't told you, you will be puzzled about why they are upset. And you won't have a chance to be with the person who is very ill.

People can get worried about what they should say or do when they're with someone ill. Usually it's OK just to be with them, without doing anything special. But if you want to say you love them, or you want to say sorry about something, this may be your last chance to say it.

When someone is dead they're not going to be hurt by being buried or burnt. Sometimes adults think a child is not old enough to understand this. But if you do, you should go to the funeral. This will help you to understand that the person has died. Children can be more frightened if somebody in the family just disappears, and they are never told that the person has died.

# Guidelines for carers and supporters

Carers and support staff working in day centres, residential homes or for community support services will find it helpful to have some guidance about what to do when someone in their care is bereaved.

If someone has a learning disability, that doesn't mean that they should be treated like a child. When someone in a person's family, a friend or a staff member is very ill, carers and supporters sometimes don't want them to be upset. So they don't tell the person what is going on. Or maybe they think that the person wouldn't understand, especially if they don't use speech or they don't know difficult words.

When someone dies who is important to the person you support, you can feel uncertain what to do, and perhaps make hasty decisions which you later regret. Different members of staff may offer contradictory advice and guidance. This is why guidelines agreed in advance are helpful, but the guidelines themselves need to be tailored to individual person's needs and wishes.

## Advice for support workers

It is preferable to talk to the client and relatives about their beliefs and wishes regarding death at your initial assessment or soon after you begin working with them. Guideline questions and a brief questionnaire are provided on the next three pages which can be adapted for your organisation. If this discussion is postponed, staff can find themselves having to ask difficult questions at a time of great stress after an unexpected serious illness or death, or staff may have to guess at the wishes of clients and relatives because there is nobody available to provide the information.

Staff sometimes worry that this appears morbid. If asked, carers usually say that they are relieved at the opportunity to discuss their wishes and make plans. They sometimes admit having worried about what would happen after a bereavement, but have not felt comfortable about discussing this with professionals.

## The following questions can be helpful when formulating guidelines

- What words, signs or other communication does the person know which will help him or her to understand the concepts of illness and death?

- Which other Books Beyond Words titles could be used to help develop the person's awareness, for example *Going into Hospital*, *Getting on with Cancer*?

- What are the person's cultural and religious beliefs?

- What preparation has been carried out by the family or others with regard to education about death?

- If the family member or friend is very elderly or ill, is the person aware that their death is approaching?

- Has the person been bereaved before or been to a funeral or cremation?

- Do staff members in your organisation accompany people to funerals?

- How and when should other clients and staff be informed of the client's bereavement?

- Should some sort of service or ritual take place in the residential home to mark the death, for example of a staff member or client?

- What memento (such as a photograph) will the client have of their friend, relative or staff member who has died?

It could be helpful to adapt the questionnaire on the next page for use in your own organisation.

# Bereavement questionnaire

Person's name

Address


Name of friend, relative or staff member who has died

Relationship to the person

Date of death

Cause of death

Cremation or burial?

Name and address of cemetery or crematorium


Did the person go to the burial or cremation? If not give reasons, if known


Has the person been to any other burial or cremation before? Give details


Give details and dates of other important losses


Who does the person live with?


If different, who did he or she live with before the bereavement?


Give details of important cultural or religious beliefs and traditions


Name of the person's own church, temple or synagogue, if any. Give name of contact, if available


Name of GP, social worker or other involved professional


*This sheet is excluded from copyright restrictions and may be photocopied*

# Useful resources

## Where to find help and advice

### Cruse Bereavement Care
Cruse is the national organisation for bereaved people. Some Cruse branches have bereavement supporters who work with children and some have supporters who work with people with learning disabilities. Cruse provides information about local bereavement counselling services and also gives welfare advice.
Helpline: 0844 477 9400
**www.cruse.org.uk**

**RD4U** is Cruse's young people's website. It is designed for young people by young people, and provides support after the death of someone close. It has a (monitored) message board and other therapeutic activities, and an email support service run by trained young volunteers.
info@rd4u.org.uk
Helpline: 0808 808 1677
**www.rd4u.org.uk**

### The Childhood Bereavement Network
Supports professionals working with bereaved children, young people and their families, through information, support and advocacy.
**www.childhoodbereavementnetwork.org.uk**

It is usually possible to access bereavement counselling through a GP, although this is often very short-term counselling. Many Community Learning Disability Teams (CLDTs) can offer bereavement counselling.

It is worth contacting local bereavement counselling services to find out whether they offer counselling to people with learning disabilities.

If they do not, this may be because they have never thought about it before. They may be prepared to, but may feel that they do not have enough knowledge. They might want to know more about what it means to have a learning disability and how they might need to extend their skills. They may decide that they would like to have some special training. This could be provided in a number of different ways:

- some advocacy and self-advocacy groups offer training about learning disability
- some Community Learning Disability Teams provide training
- the training could be provided by a specialist training service.

Since 2005, everyone in England who has a learning disability has been encouraged to have a health action plan. A bereavement need could be included in a person's health action plan, which would then mean that they should be supported to get any help they need in order to access bereavement counselling.

For more information about health action plans see *Action for Health – Health Action Plans and Health Facilitation*, which contains detailed good practice guidance. Available free from the Department of Health. An easy read version for people with learning disabilities is also available:
**learning disabilitynurse.com/wp-content uploads/2012/02/health-action-plans1/pdf**

## Written information

*Am I Allowed to Cry? A Study of Bereavement amongst People who have Learning Difficulties* by Maureen Oswin. £12.99. Souvenir Press, London.

*Loss and Learning Disability* by Noëlle Blackman. This book is for support workers, therapists and counsellors working with people with learning disabilities, showing how they can be affected by bereavement. It includes ways to prevent normal grief from becoming a bigger problem and to help people when the grief process 'goes wrong'. £19.99. Worth Publishing, London.

*What on Earth Do You Do When Someone Dies?* by Trevor Romain and Elizabeth Verdick. This book aims to help with some of the questions that children struggle with following a bereavement. Each section addresses a different question, including: Why do people have to die? Am I going to die too? Is the death my fault? What can I do if I'm angry? Is it still OK to have fun? The book could be read by an adult to a child, but older children might benefit from reading it on their own. £5.99. Freespirit Publishing, Minneapolis.

*Badger's Parting Gifts* by Susan Varley. An illustrated book about a wise old badger. When he dies the other animals miss him, but he lives on in all they learned from him. Aimed at children. £6.99. Andersen Press.

*Supporting Bereaved Children*. A booklet for adults caring for a bereaved child. This short booklet describes and seeks to explain some of the ways in which bereavement can affect children's behaviour, and the support they may find most helpful. £2.45 from Cruse Bereavement. **www.crusebereavement.eu/publications/cruse-bookstore/all**

Cruse Bereavement Care also offers a selection of free booklets on bereavement aimed at both young people and adults.

*After Someone Dies*. A booklet about death, bereavement and grief for young people of secondary school age.

*Supporting Children Through Grief*. A leaflet for parents and carers.

**www.crusebereavement.eu/publications/booklets**

**Video**

*Coping with Death*. Explains what happens when somebody dies, and shows adults with learning disabilities coping with death. £30 (inc. p&p) from Speak Up Self Advocacy. The DVD can be ordered direct from the catalogue:

**www.friendlyresource.org.uk**.

## Related titles in the Books Beyond Words series

*When Mum Died* (2014, 4th edition) by Sheila Hollins and Lester Sireling, illustrated by Beth Webb. A partner book to *When Dad Died*, showing a family dealing with the loss of a mother. This book shows a burial.

*When Somebody Dies* (2014, 2nd edition) by Sheila Hollins, Sandra Dowling and Noëlle Blackman, illustrated by Catherine Brighton. Shows how a man and a woman are helped by regular bereavement counselling sessions, and the comfort and companionship shown by friends, to learn to feel less sad and to cope with life better and better as time passes.

*Am I Going to Die?* (2009) by Sheila Hollins and Irene Tuffrey-Wijne, illustrated by Lisa Kopper. Tells the story of John, who has a terminal illness. It deals with physical deterioration and the emotional aspects of dying in an honest and moving way.

*Getting On With Cancer* (2002) by Veronica Donaghy, Jane Bernal, Irene Tuffrey-Wijne and Sheila Hollins, illustrated by Beth Webb. Designed to help people who become unwell and are diagnosed as having cancer. This book deals honestly with the unpleasant side of treatment, including chemotherapy and radiotherapy, and ends on a positive note.

*Looking After my Heart* (2005) by Sheila Hollins, Francesco Cappuccio and Paul Adeline, illustrated by Lisa Kopper. A book about Jane, who smokes and eats unhealthily and suffers a heart attack. After tests, she is given medication, changes her lifestyle, and recovers fully.

*Sonia's Feeling Sad* (2011) by Sheila Hollins and Roger Banks, illustrated by Lisa Kopper. Sonia is feeling so sad that she shuts herself off from her family and friends. She agrees to see a counsellor and gradually begins to feel better.

*Ron's Feeling Blue* (2011, 2nd edition) by Sheila Hollins, Roger Banks and Jenny Curran, illustrated by Beth Webb. When Ron retires to bed and shuns his friends, his GP arranges to see him regularly. She helps Ron to enjoy life again.

## Books Beyond Words

A wide range of other titles is available in this series. See **www.booksbeyondwords.co.uk**

# Authors

**Sheila Hollins** is Emeritus Professor of Psychiatry of Disability at St George's, University of London, and sits in the House of Lords. She is a past President and an Honorary Fellow of the Royal College of Psychiatrists. She is founding editor of Books Beyond Words and Executive Chair of Beyond Words.

**Lester Sireling** is a consultant psychiatrist with many years' experience of working with people with learning disabilities.

**Beth Webb** is an artist with a background in psychology and sociology who specialises in alternative communication media. She has pioneered the use of emotional colour and mime in her illustrations for the Books Beyond Words series.

## Dedication

For our children:

Kathryn and Nigel Hollins, Emily Westlake and Abigail Witchalls

Ben, Rachel, Yoni, Abi and Aviva Sireling.

# Beyond Words: publications and training

Books Beyond Words will help family carers, support workers and professionals working with people who find pictures easier than words for understanding their world. A list of all Beyond Words publications, including Books Beyond Words titles, and where to buy them, can be found on our website:
**www.booksbeyondwords.co.uk**
email: **admin@booksbeyondwords.co.uk**

Workshops about using Books Beyond Words are provided regularly in London, or can be arranged in other localities on request. For information about forthcoming workshops see our website. Self-advocates are welcome.

Video clips showing our books being read are also on our website and YouTube channel:
**www.youtube.com/user/booksbeyondwords** and on our DVD, *How to Use Books Beyond Words*.

# How to read 'When Dad Died'

There is no right or wrong way to read this book. Remember it is not necessary to be able to read the words.

1. Some people are not used to reading books. Start at the beginning and read the story in each picture.

2. Whether you are reading the book with one person or with a group, encourage them to tell the story in their own words. You will discover what each person thinks is happening, what they already know, and how they feel. You may think something different is happening in the pictures yourself, but that doesn't matter. Wait to see if their ideas change as the story develops. Don't challenge the reader(s) or suggest their ideas are wrong.

3. Some pictures may be more difficult to understand. It can help to prompt the people you are supporting, for example:

- Who do you think that is?
- What is happening?
- What is he or she doing now?
- How is he or she feeling?
- Do you feel like that? Has it happened to you/ your friend/ your family?

4. You don't have to read the whole book in one sitting. Allow people enough time to follow the pictures at their own pace.

5. Some people will not be able to follow the story, but they may be able to understand some of the pictures. Stay a little longer with the pictures that interest them.